Allison,

Congratulations on your graduation! I hope this to mark those special days and memories your first year away.

With fondest wishes,

Dr. Clayden

The Way of the Tranquil Heart Book of Special Days

Los Angeles
County Museum
of Art

Universe

The Pavilion for Japanese
Art at the Los Angeles
County Museum of Art

Published by
Universe Books
381 Park Avenue South
New York, NY 10016

Coordinated and designed by Sandy Bell
Edited by Mitch Tuchman

The Edo period was a remarkable time in the history of Japan, an unbroken stretch of peace and order during which the country developed the unique identity we have come to know. Art flourished with a vitality not seen before or since and found a new expression that was distinctly Japanese: subtle and simple as the artists' skill could make it, existing for no purpose but to delight the eye.

The Shin'enkan Collection is the finest collection of Edo-period painting in the Western world. It has come to the Los Angeles County Museum of Art as the gift of the collectors, Mr. and Mrs. Joe D. Price. Unmatched for its superb quality and breadth of schools and styles included, the collection contains both the early and late works of individual masters, works by their students, contemporary and posthumous imitations, and occasional original works by the imitators as well.

This distinguished array represents a far-reaching resource for continuous exhibition and study at the Pavilion for Japanese Art at the Los Angeles County Museum. The pavilion, designed by the late Bruce Goff, is in an exciting, interesting, and sensitive building in which the art is displayed to its best advantage. The generosity of the community at large, matched by the further magnanimity of the Prices, has made possible the realization of this dream.

Earl A. Powell III
Director

1

2

Suzuki Kiitsu
(1796–1858)
New Year's Decoration
(detail)
Hanging scroll
Color on silk
113 x 42 cm
(44½ x 16½ in.)

3

4

5

6

7

8

Teisai Hokuba
(1771–1844)
*Two Beauties by the Sumida
River in Spring* (detail)
Hanging scroll
Color on silk
103.1 x 33.7 cm
(40⅝ x 13¼ in.)

9

10

I I

I 2

I 3

I 4

I 5

I 6

Itō Jakuchū (1716–1800)
Birds, Animals,
and Flowering Plants
(detail)
Pair of six-fold screens
Color on paper
Each 167 x 376 cm
(65¾ x 148 in.)

I 7

18 _____

19 _____

20 _____

21 _____

22 _____

23 _____

24 _____

Katsukawa Shunshō
(1726–92)
Two Beauties (detail)
Hanging scroll
Color on silk
100.2 x 35.2 cm
(39⁹⁄₁₆ x 13⁷⁄₈ in.)

25

26

27

28

29

30

Maruyama Ōshin
(1790–1838)
*Dragon Emerging
from the Sea* (detail)
Hanging scroll
Ink on silk
30.5 x 15 cm
(12 x 5¹⁵⁄₁₆ in.)

31

FEBRUARY ·

——————————————— 1

——————————————— 2

——————————————— 3

——————————————— 4

——————————————— 5

——————————————— 6

Itō Jakuchū (1716 – 1800)
Tiger (detail), 1755
Hanging scroll
Color on silk
130.3 x 71.4 cm
(51⁵⁄₁₆ x 28⅛ in.)

——————————————— 7

8 ─────────────────────────

9 ─────────────────────────

10 ─────────────────────────

11 ─────────────────────────

12 ─────────────────────────

13 ─────────────────────────

Anonymous
*Red and White Blossoming
Plum Trees* (detail)
Seventeenth century
Pair of six-fold screen
Color on paper
Each 153.3 x 346.8 cm
(60⅜ x 136⁹⁄₁₆ in.)

14 ─────────────────────────

15

16

17

18

19

Nakamura Hōchū
(fl. late 18th –
early 19th century)
Fans (detail)
Two-fold screen
Color on paper
167 x 172 cm
(65¾ x 67¾ in.)

20

21

22

23

24

25

26

27

Anonymous
Tale of Genji (detail)
Seventeenth century
Pair of six-fold screens
Color with gold ground
on paper
Each 152.5 x 347.4 cm
(60 x 136¾ in.)

28

29

1

2

3

4

Anonymous
Pleasure Quarter Scenes
(detail)
Seventeenth century
Pair of eight-fold screens
Color with gold ground
on paper
Each 162 x 362 cm
(63¾ x 142½ in.)

5

6

MARCH ·

7 _____

8 _____

9 _____

10 _____

11 _____

12 _____

Unkoku Tōteki (d. 1626)
*Birds and Flowers
of the Four Seasons* (detail)
Pair of six-fold screens
Color with gold ground
on paper
Each 129.6 x 295.2 cm
(51 x 116⅛ in.)

13 _____

MARCH·

14

15

16

17

18

Mori Sosen (1747–1821)
Monkeys and Plum Tree
(detail)
Hanging scroll
Ink and color on silk
89.8 x 33.6 cm
(35⅜ x 13¼ in.)

19

20

21

22

23

24

25

26

Suzuki Kiitsu
(1796–1858)
Dancing (detail)
Hanging scroll
Color on silk
105.9 x 49.7 cm
(41⅞₁₆ x 19⅞₁₆ in.)

27

28

29

30

31

1

Anonymous
*Birds and Flowers
of the Four Seasons*
(detail)
Seventeenth century
Pair of six-fold screens
Color on paper
Each 151.6 x 364.0 cm
(59^{11}/$_{16}$ x 143^{3}/$_{8}$ in.)

2

3

4 _____

5 _____

6 _____

7 _____

8 _____

9 _____

Maruyama Ōkyo
signature and seals
*Two Phoenixes
on a Paulownia Tree*
(detail)
Hanging scroll
Color on silk
126 x 57.3 cm
(49⅝ x 22½ in.)

10 _____

11 ——————————————

12 ——————————————

13 ——————————————

14 ——————————————

15 ——————————————

16 ——————————————

Suzuki Kiitsu
Spring and Summer
Flowers and Grasses (detail)
Hanging scroll
Color on silk
91 x 35 cm
(35⅞ x 13¾ in.)

17 ——————————————

18

19

20

21

22

23

Katsukawa Shunrin
(fl. 1784–1800)
Five Beauties (detail)
Hanging scroll
Color on silk
55 x 33 cm
(21⅝ x 12 in.)

24

25

26

27

28

29

30

Nagasawa Rosetsu
(1754–99)
Peacock and Peonies
(detail), 1781
Two-fold screen
Color on paper
165.5 x 184 cm
(65³⁄₁₆ x 72⁷⁄₁₆ in.)

I

2

3

4

5

6

7

Yoshimura Kōkei
(1769–1836)
Tiger (detail)
Hanging scroll
Ink on silk
103. 5 x 32 cm
(40¾ x 12⅝ in.)

8

9

10

11

12

13

Sakai Hōitsu (1761–1828)
Birds and Flowers
of the Twelve Months: May
(detail)
Twelve hanging scrolls
Color on silk
Each 140.2 x 50.3 cm
(55³⁄₁₆ x 19¹³⁄₁₆ in.)

14

15

16 _____

17 _____

18 _____

19 _____

20 _____

21 _____

Masahiro
(dates unknown)
One Hundred Women
(detail)
Hanging scroll
Color on silk
113.6 x 42.3 cm
(44¾ x 16⅝ in.)

22 _____

23 _____

24 _____

25 _____

26 _____

27 _____

Shiba Kōkan (1747–1818)
signature and seals
Insects and Plants (detail)
Pair of hanging scrolls
Color on silk
25.1 x 19.2 cm
(9⅞ x 7½ in.)

28 _____

29 _____

30

31

1

2

3

4

Anonymous
Pleasure Quarter Scenes
(detail)
Seventeenth century
Pair of eight–fold screens
Color with gold ground
on paper
Each 162 x 362 cm
(63¾ x 142½ in.)

5

6

7

8

9

10

Anonymous
Fish Trap (detail)
Seventeenth century
Pair of six-fold screens
Color with gold ground
on paper
Each 162.5 x 359 cm
(63 x 141⅜ in.)

11

12

13 —————————————————————

14 —————————————————————

15 —————————————————————

16 —————————————————————

17 —————————————————————

18 —————————————————————

Sakai Hōitsu (1761–1828)
*Birds and Flowers
of the Twelve Months: June*
(detail)
Twelve hanging scrolls
Color on silk
Each 140.2 x 50.3 cm
(55⁵⁄₁₆ x 19¹³⁄₁₆ in.)

19 —————————————————————

20

21

22

23

24

Suzuki Kiitsu
(1796–1858)
Seashells and Plums (detail)
Hanging scroll
Color on silk
34.8 x 29.2 cm
(13¹¹⁄₁₆ x 11½ in.)

25

26

27

28

29

30

1

2

3

Tsubaki Chinzan
(1801 – 54)
Carp (detail)
Hanging scroll
Color on silk
55.0 x 69.9 cm
(21^{11}/₁₆ x 27½ in.)

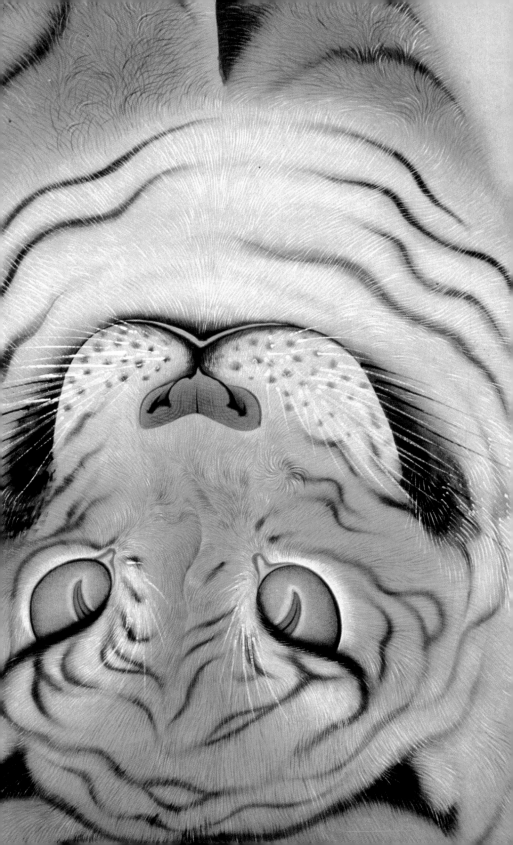

4

5

6

7

8

Maruyama Ōkyo (attrib.)
(1733–95)
Tiger (detail), 1785
Hanging scroll
Color on silk
114.1 x 25.3 cm
(44^{15}/$_{16}$ x 9^{15}/$_{16}$ in.)

9

10

11 _____

12 _____

13 _____

14 _____

15 _____

16 _____

Sakai Hōitsu (1761–1828)
The Thirty-six Poets
(detail)
Two-fold screen
Color with gold ground
on paper
165.3 x 180.6 cm
(65⅛ x 71⅛ in.)

17 _____

JULY ·

18

19

20

21

22

Suzuki Kiitsu
(1796–1858)
Egret and Willow (detail)
Two-fold screen
Color on silk
132.3 x 141.5 cm
(52⅛ x 55¹¹⁄₁₆ in.)

23

24

25

26

27

28

29

30

Anonymous
*A Daimyō's Procession
through Seta* (detail)
Seventeenth century
Six-fold screen
Color on paper
159.8 x 363.1 cm
(62⅞ x 142¹⁵⁄₁₆ in.)

31

AUGUST ·

1

2

3

4

5

6

Anonymous
Famous Places of Kyoto
(detail)
Early eighteenth century
Eight-fold screen
Color with gold ground
on paper
92.8 x 365 cm
(36½ x 143¾ in.)

7

8 _____

9 _____

10 _____

11 _____

12 _____

13 _____

14 _____

Okamoto Shūki
(1807–62)
Swallows and Waves
(detail)
Hanging scroll
Ink and color on silk
130.3 x 56.1 cm
(51 9/16 x 22 1/8 in.)

15 _____

16 _____

17 _____

18 _____

19 _____

Itō Jakuchū (1716–1800)
Rooster, Hen,
and Hydrangeas (detail)
Hanging scroll
Color on silk
139.4 x 85.4 cm
(54⅞ x 33⅜ in.)

20 _____

21 _____

AUGUST·

22

23

24

25

26

27

Maruyama Ōshin
(1790–1838)
Rice and Barley (detail)
Pair of six-fold screens
Color with gold ground
on paper
Each 156.7 x 362.6 cm
(61 11/16 x 142 3/4 in.)

28

29

30

31

1

2

Nakamura Hōchō
(fl. late 18th–
early 19th century)
Suzuki Kiitsu
(1796–1858)
Fans (detail)
Two-fold screen
Color with gold ground
on paper
154.9 x 166.4 cm
(61 x 65½ in.)

3

4

5

6

7

8

9

10

Kitagawa Sōsetsu (attrib.)
(fl. mid–17th century)
*Poppy Flowers, Thistles,
and Chinese Milk Vetches*
(detail)
Hanging scroll
Color on paper
121.1 x 48.1 cm
(47¾ x 18¹⁵⁄₁₆ in.)

11

12

13

14

15

16

Sakai Dōitsu
A Quail amid Autumn
Flowers and Grasses
under a Full Moon
(detail)
Late nineteenth century
Hanging scroll
Color on silk
49.5 x 63 cm
(19½ x 24¾ in.)

17

18

19

20

21

22

23

24

Kaigetsudō School
Beauty (detail)
Eighteenth century
Hanging scroll
Color on paper
94.5 x 37.5 cm
(37¼ x 14¾ in.)

25

26

27

28

29

30

Sakai Hōitsu (1761 – 1828)
Sweeping Maple Leaves
(detail)
Hanging scroll
Color on silk
110.5 x 46.5 cm
(43½ x 18⅝₁₆ in.)

1

2

OCTOBER ·

3

4

5

6

7

8

Suzuki Kiitsu
(1796 – 1858)
Paulownia and Maple
(detail)
Pair of hanging scrolls
Color on silk
Each 119.7 x 35.6 cm
(47⅛ x 14 in.)

9

OCTOBER ·

10

11

12

13

14

Suzuki Kiitsu
(1796–1858)
Tanabata (detail)
Hanging scroll
Color on silk
110.9 x 39.3 cm
(43¹¹⁄₁₆ x 15⁵⁄₁₆ in.)

15

16

17

18

19

20

21

22

Anonymous
Gibbons (detail)
Seventeenth century
Two-fold screen
Ink on paper
152.4 x 175.2 cm
(60 x 69 in.)

23

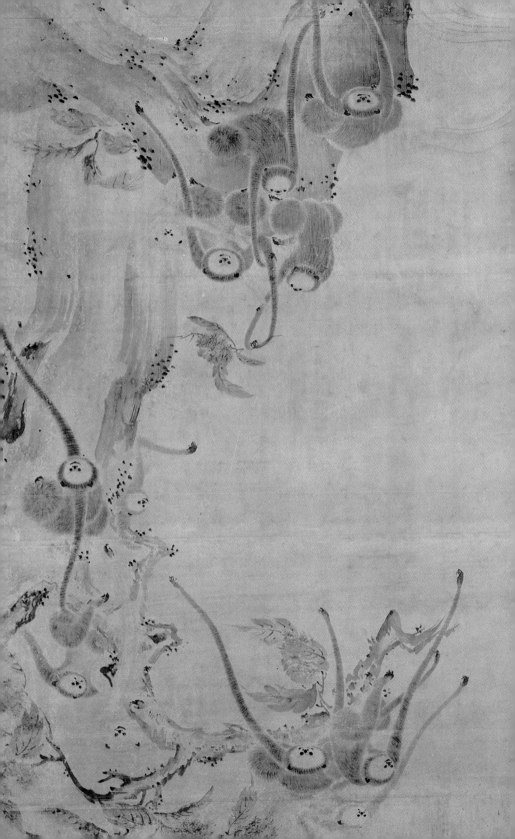

OCTOBER ·

24

25

26

27

28

Shibata Zeshin (1807–91)
*Hawk Perched
on a Snow-covered Branch*
(detail)
Hanging scroll
Color on silk
109.2 x 40.8 cm
(43 x 16⅟₁₆ in.)

29

30

31

1

2

3

4

5

Suzuki Kiitsu
(1796–1858)
*Plovers and Waves
under a Full Moon* (detail)
Hanging scroll
Ink and color on silk
82.7 x 26.5 cm
(32½ x 10½ in.)

6

7

8

9

10

11

Itō Jakuchū (1716–1800)
*Birds, Animals,
and Flowering Plants*
(detail)
Pair of six-fold screens
Color on paper
Each 167 x 376 cm
(65¾ x 148 in.)

12

13

14 _____

15 _____

16 _____

17 _____

18 _____

19 _____

Anonymous
Pheasants and Bamboo
(detail)
Eighteenth century
Four sliding screens
Color with gold ground
on paper
Each panel 169 x 94 cm
(66½ x 37 in.)

20 _____

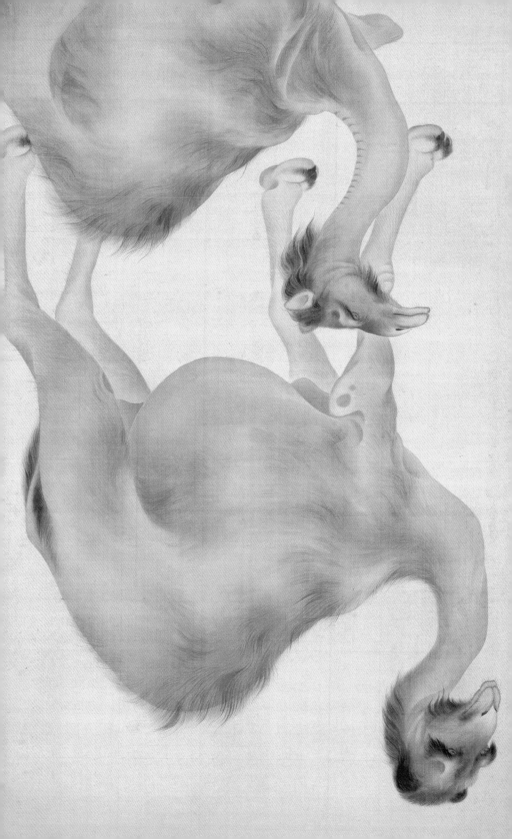

21

22

23

24

25

26

Maruyama Ōshin
(1790–1838)
Two Camels (detail), 1824
Hanging scroll
Color on silk
125.3 x 57.3 cm
(49⅜ x 22⁹⁄₁₆ in.)

27

28 ——————————————————————

29 ——————————————————————

30 ——————————————————————

1 ——————————————————————

2 ——————————————————————

3 ——————————————————————

Kitagawa Kikumaro
(d. 1830)
Two Beauties (detail)
Hanging scroll
Color on paper
124.7 x 55.8 cm
(49⅛ x 22 in.)

4 ——————————————————————

5

6

7

8

9

Sakai Hōitsu (1761–1828)
*Birds and Flowers
of the Twelve Months:
December* (detail)
Twelve hanging scrolls
Color on silk
Each 140.2 x 50.3 cm
(55³⁄₁₆ x 19¹³⁄₁₆ in.)

10

11

12 ————————————————————

13 ————————————————————

14 ————————————————————

15 ————————————————————

16 ————————————————————

17 ————————————————————

Itō Jakuchū (1716–1800)
Mandarin Ducks
amid Snow-covered Reeds
(detail)
Hanging scroll
Color on silk
110.7 x 51.5 cm
(43⅝ x 20¼ in.)

18 ————————————————————

DECEMBER ·

19

20

21

22

23

Katsu Jagyoku (1733–78)
Crows and Plum Tree,
Rabbits and Pine Trees
in Snow (detail), 1774
Pair of six-fold screens
Ink and white pigment
on paper
Each 153.8 x 353.0 cm
(60⁹⁄₁₆ x 138¹⁵⁄₁₆ in.)

24

25

$\cdot$ DECEMBER $\cdot$

26 _____

27 _____

28 _____

29 _____

30 _____

31 _____

_____

ADDRESSES

NOTES